The Classical Piano Method
Finger Fitness 2

Hans-Günter Heumann

ED 13552

www.schott-music.com

SCHOTT

Mainz · London · Madrid · New York · Paris · Prague · Tokyo · Toronto
© 2013 Schott Music Ltd, London · Printed in Germany

ED 13552
British Library Cataloguing-in-Publication Data.
A catalogue record for this book is available
from the British Library
ISMN 979-0-2201-3407-4
ISBN 978-1-84761-291-5

Cover design by www.adamhaystudio.com
Cover photography: iStockphoto

Music setting and layout by Wega Verlag GmbH
Printed in Germany S&Co.8899

FIVE TOP PRACTICE TIPS

1. Establishing a good playing posture is a great start on the road to developing a good technique and sound. Firstly sit in an upright, but relaxed position at the centre of the keyboard, and towards the front edge of the stool. Your hands should comfortably reach the keys. Make sure your arms are relaxed and the shoulders are not raised. Your fingers should be positioned so that the forearm, wrist and backs of the hands form a straight line. Also your fingers should be softly curved as if holding a ball. Make sure to adjust your stool to the correct height! Too high and your back will arch, too low and your shoulders will rise. You should sit so that the upper body is balanced and stable. Certain muscle groups, such as those in the neck and shoulders should be consciously relaxed.

2. Practice as slowly as you need to play without mistakes or hesitation, then gradually increase the tempo.

3. Practice first with each hand separately, then with both hands together.

4. You will learn more quickly if you practice in small sections or passages. Study the piece, looking for repetitions and similarities. Problem passages should always be practiced on their own, and repeated many times. After that, it is important to practice them in context. Additionally, through practicing in this way you can learn to play the pieces from memory.

5. From time to time, play or think through the pieces and hear the music in your head. In your mind's eye, imagine either the score itself or the fingers with which you play the notes.

Hans-Günter Heumann

CONTENTS

1. Easiest Pieces

Op. 190, No. 13

Christian Louis Heinrich Köhler (1820-1886)

Op. 190, No. 14

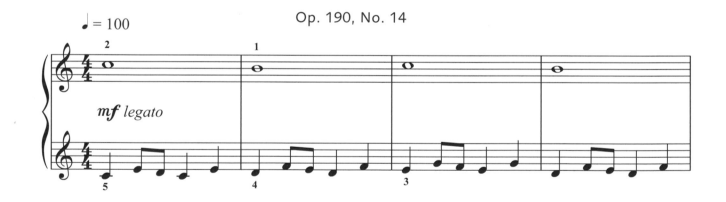

Op. 190, No. 16

2. Repetition Sixths

3. Changes between Two Neighbouring Sixths

♩ = 100

Hans-Günter Heumann

4. Singing Sixths

Hans-Günter Heumann

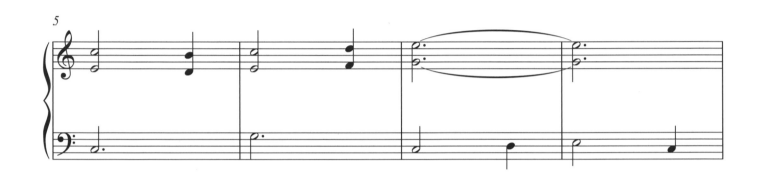

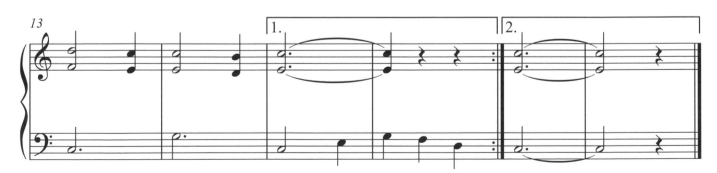

5. Finger Strength and Equalization of all Fingers: 1

Two Exercises from *L'ABC du Piano*

♩ = 120–168
No. 65

Félix Le Couppey (1811–1887)

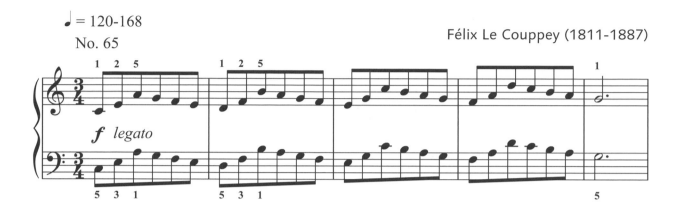

No. 66

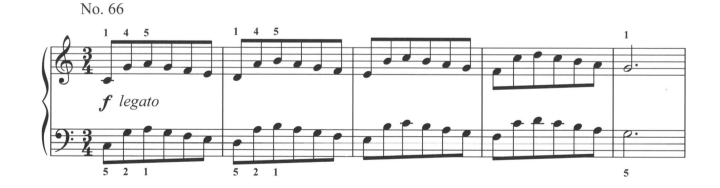

6. Intervals from a Second to an Octave

Hans-Günter Heumann

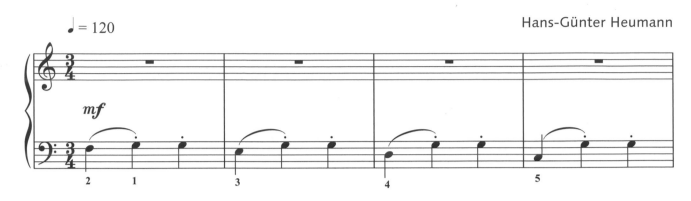

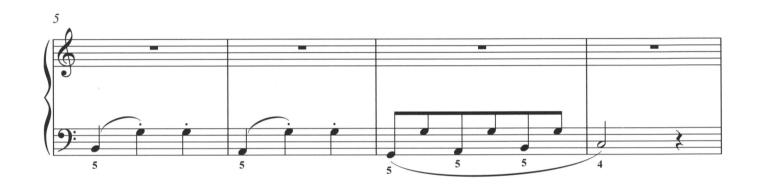

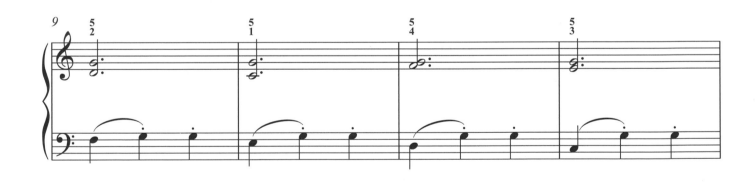

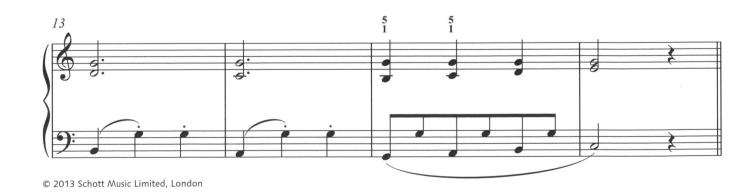

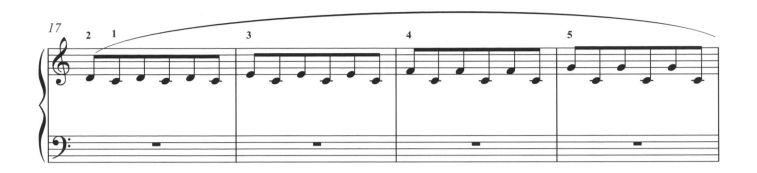

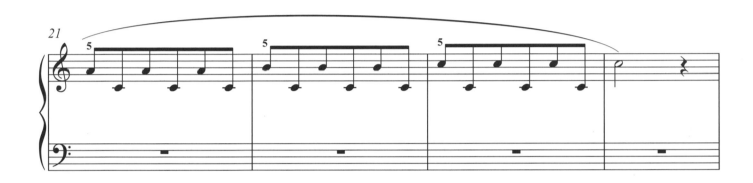

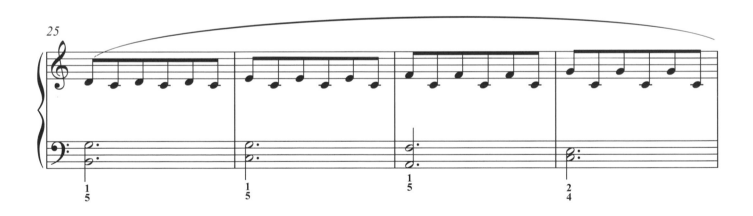

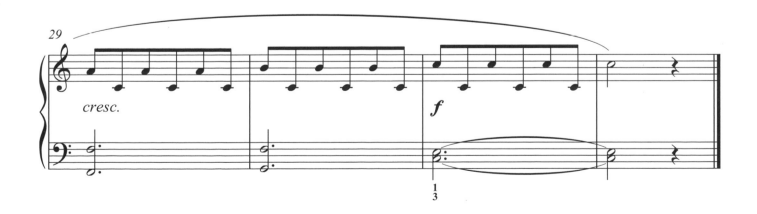

7. The Little Meeting

Study Op. 100, No. 4
Double Notes with Thirds and Sixths

*) *Staccatissimo* can be notated with a little spike above or below a note, and should be played as an extremely short, detached *staccato*.

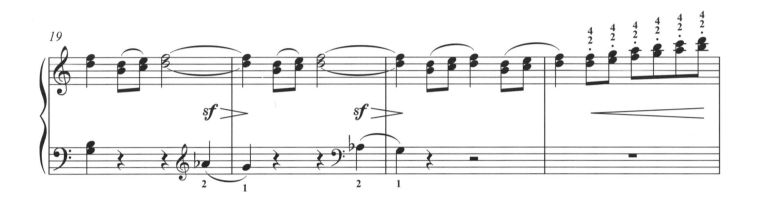

8. Finger Changes on the Same Key

♩ = 120

Hans-Günter Heumann

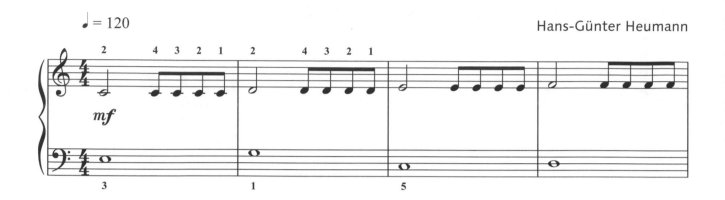

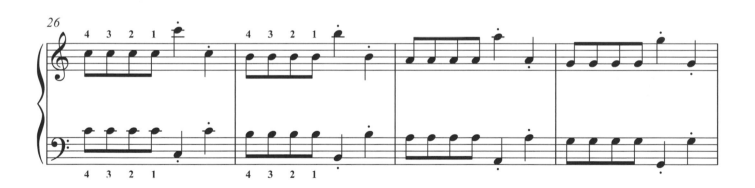

9. Passing the Thumb Under the Third Finger

Hans-Günter Heumann

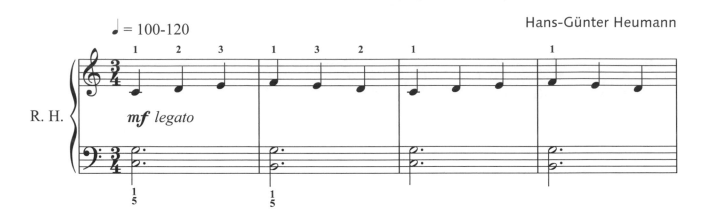

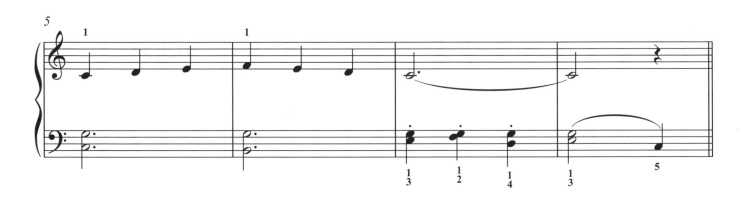

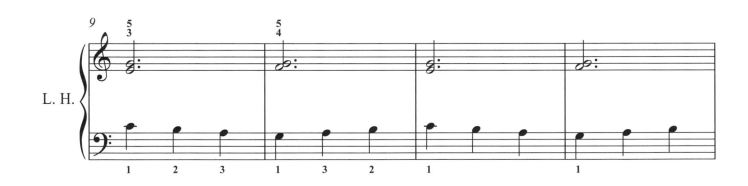

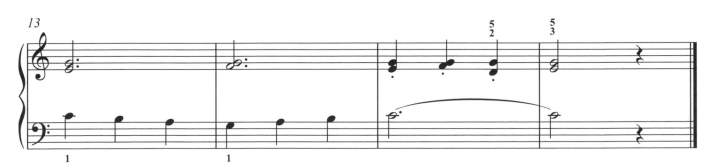

10. Passing the Third Finger Over the Thumb

♩ = 80-100

Hans-Günter Heumann

R. H.

mf legato

L. H.

11. Finger Strength and Equalization of all Fingers: 2

The Virtuoso Pianist, Exercise No. 1

Charles-Louis Hanon (1819-1900)

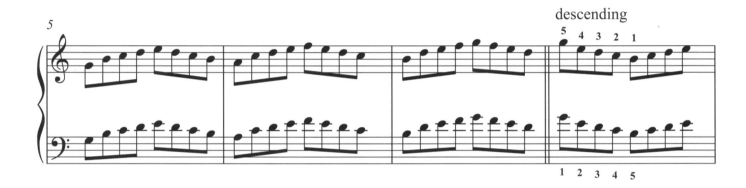

12. Finger Strength and Equalization of the Weaker Fingers

Hans-Günter Heumann

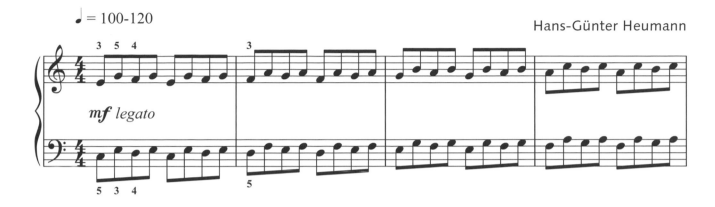

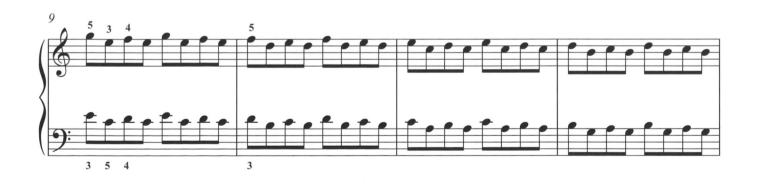

13. Preparatory Exercises

Hans-Günter Heumann

14. Scale Etude

Transpose this piece also as a G Major Scale (see p. 48) and as an F Major Scale (see p. 58).

Hans-Günter Heumann

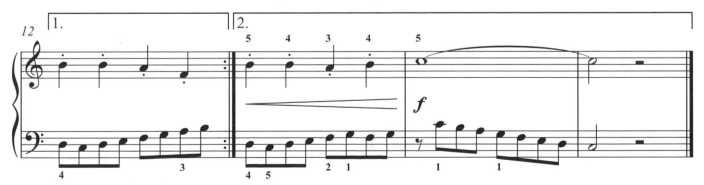

15. Scales in Contrary Motion

Transpose this piece also in G Major Scale (see p. 48) and F Major Scale (see p. 58).

Hans-Günter Heumann

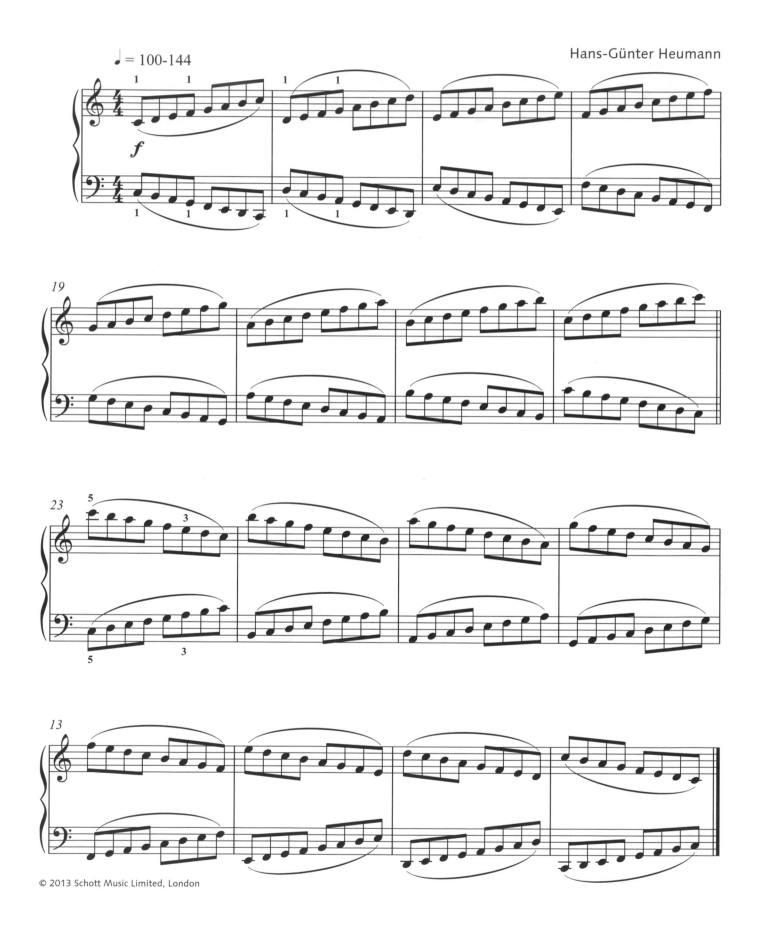

16. Scales in Parallel Motion

Transpose this piece also in G Major Scale (see p. 48) and F Major Scale (see p. 58).

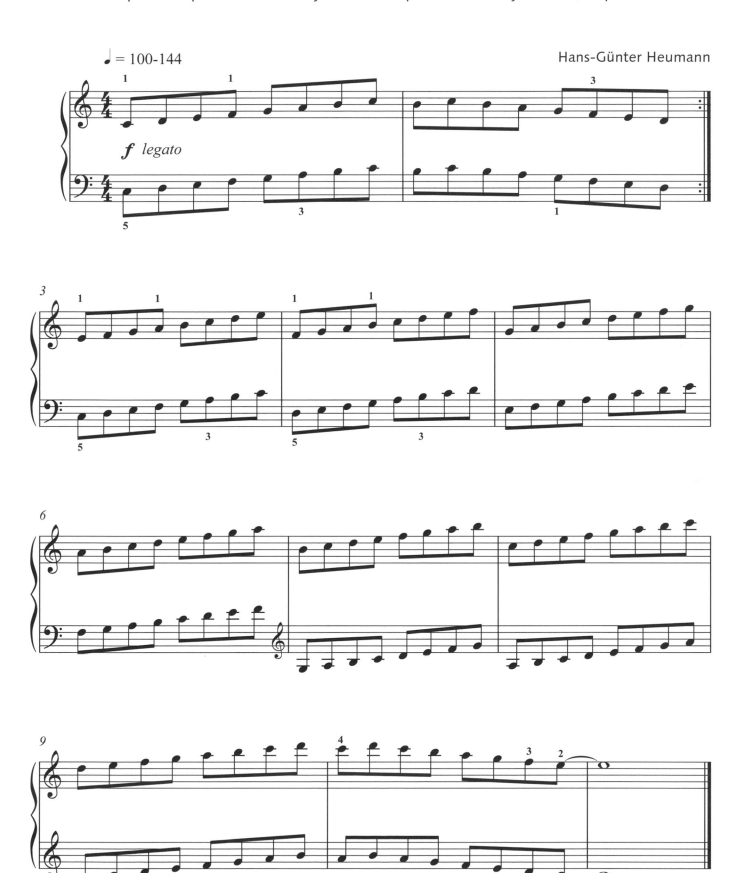

17. Scales Over Two Octaves

Transpose this piece also in G Major Scale (see p. 48) and F Major Scale (see p. 58).

Hans-Günter Heumann

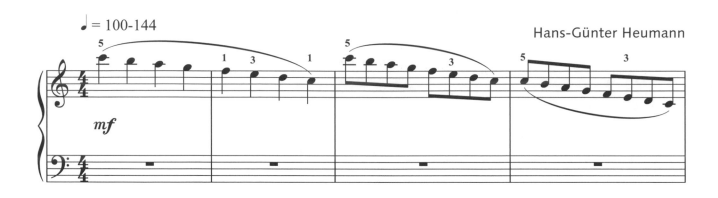

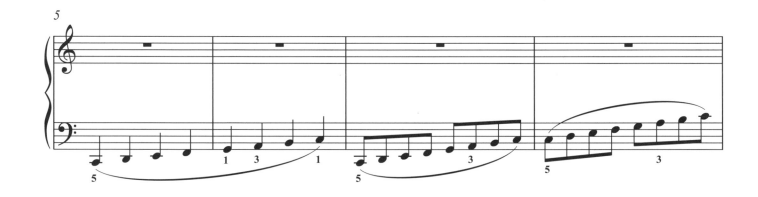

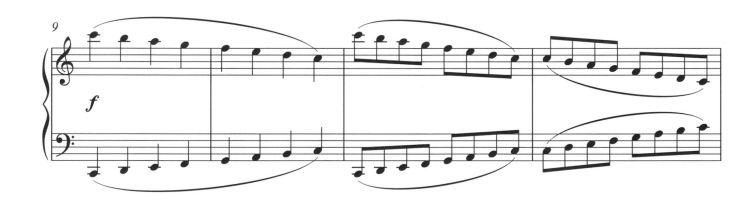

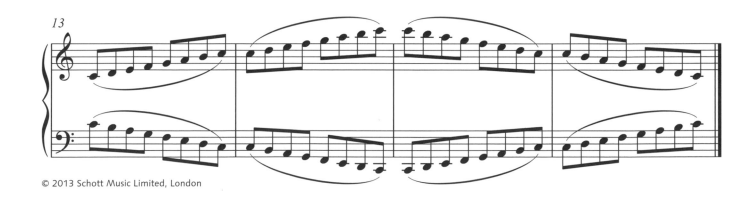

18. Preparatory School

Op. 101, No. 65

Moderato ♩ = 108-120

Ferdinand Beyer (1803-1863)

f sempre legato

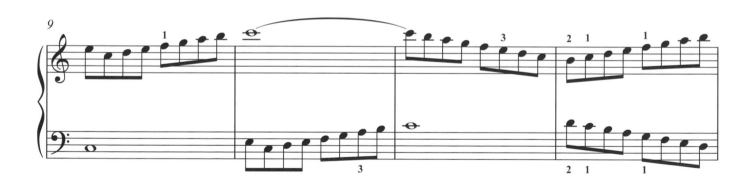

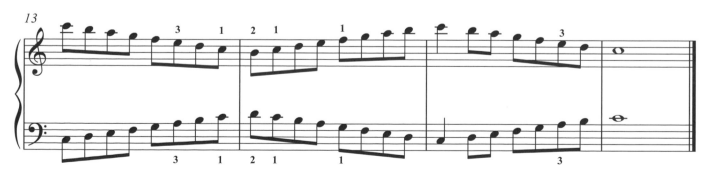

19. Grand Arpeggio Etude

Chord Study: 1

Hans-Günter Heumann

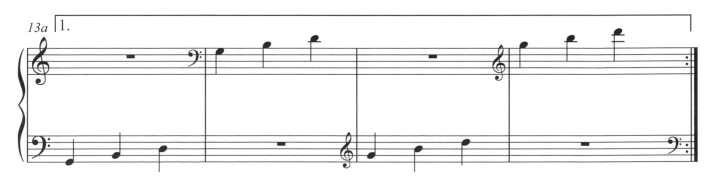

20. Block Chords and Broken Chords

Chord Study: 2

Hans-Günter Heumann

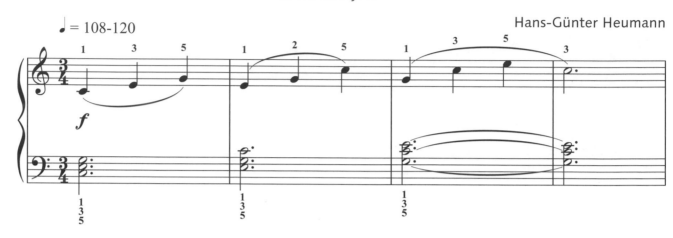

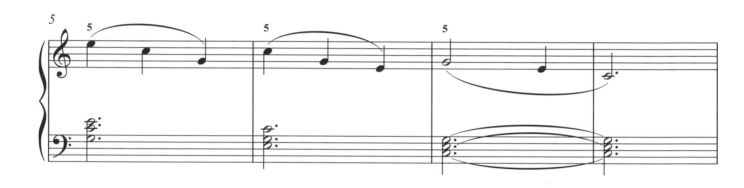

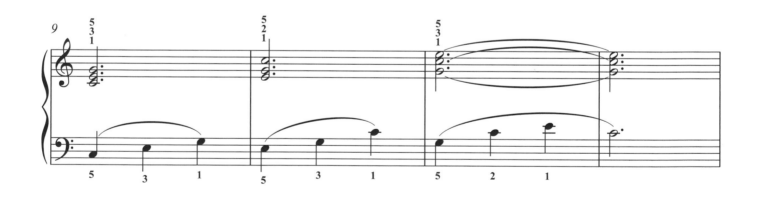

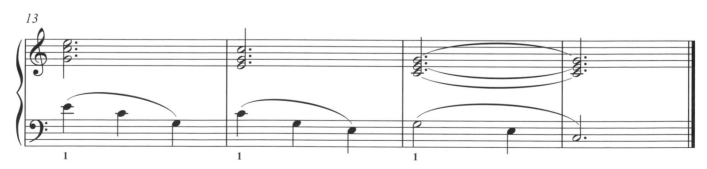

21. Interchange between the Hands: 1

Chord Study: 3

Hans-Günter Heumann

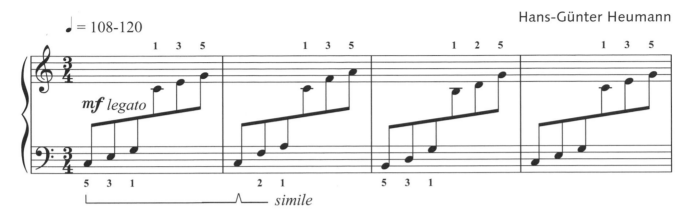

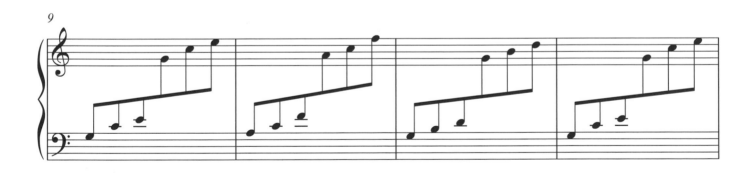

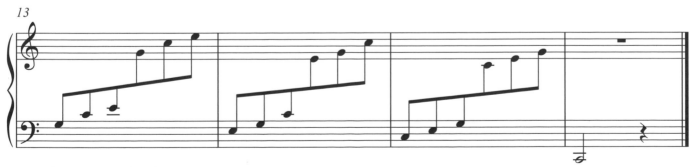

22. Elementary Study

Op. 176, No. 4

Evenness Study: 1

Moderato ♩ = 108-120

Jean-Baptiste Duvernoy (1800-1880)

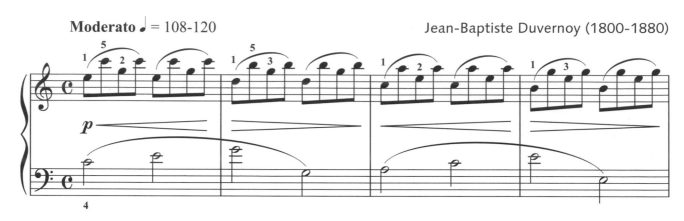

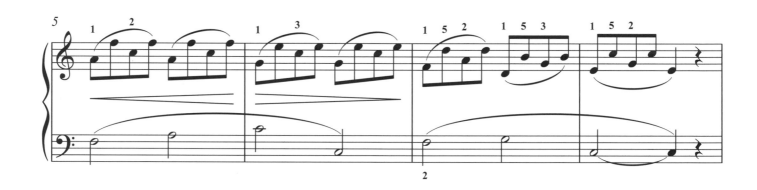

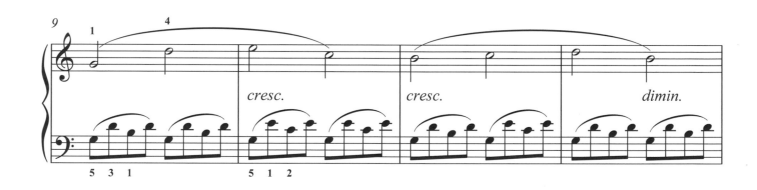

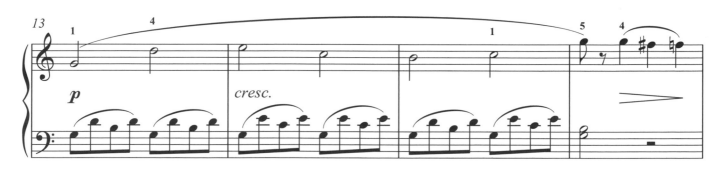

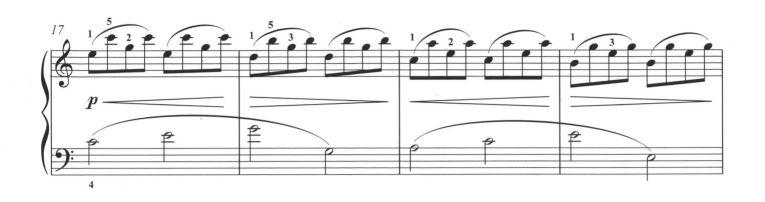

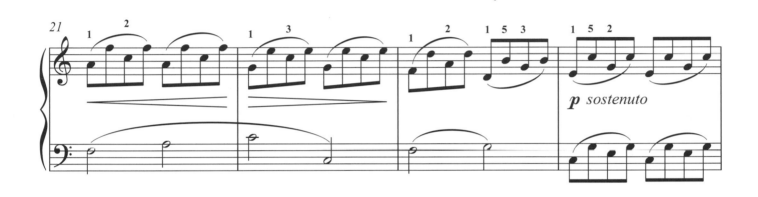

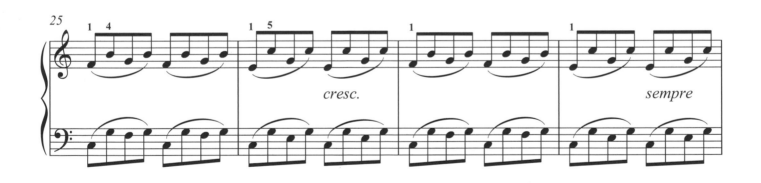

23. Étude Enfantine

Op. 37, No. 1

Velocity Study: 1

Jean-Henry Lemoine (1786-1854)

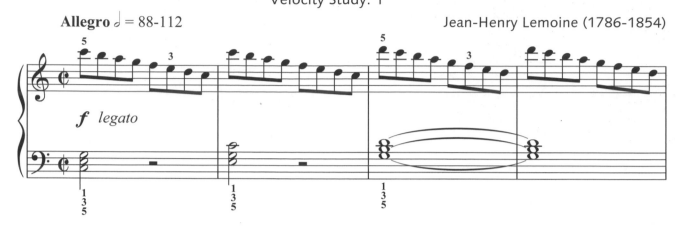

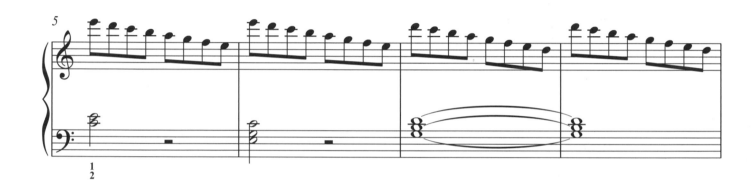

24. Étude Enfantine

Op. 37, No. 2

Velocity Study: 2

Jean-Henry Lemoine (1786-1854)

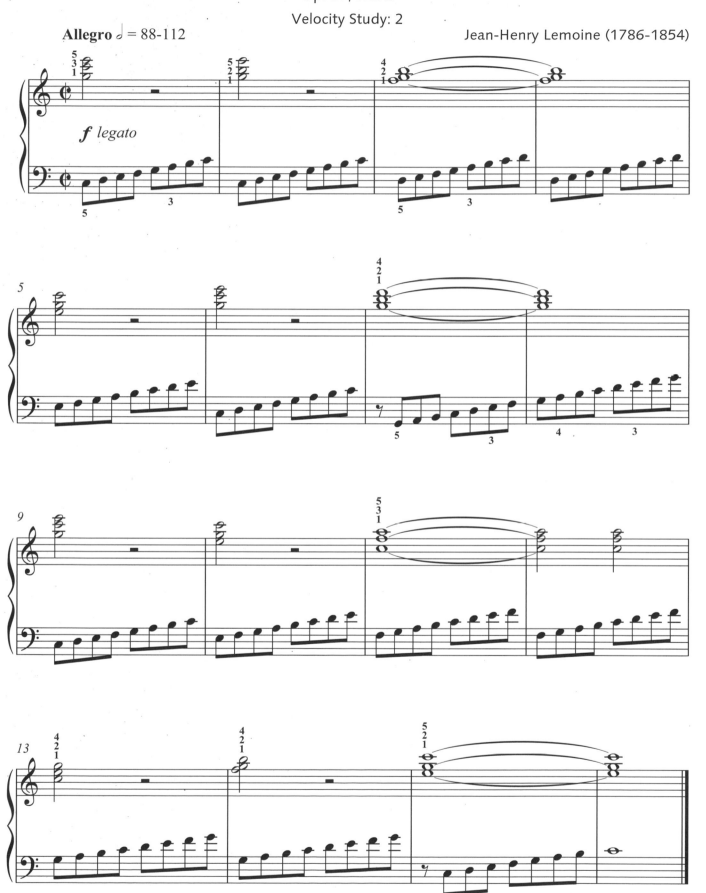

25. The Little Pianist

Op. 823, No. 43

Carl Czerny (1791-1857)

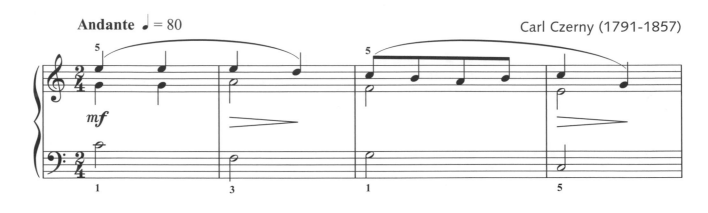

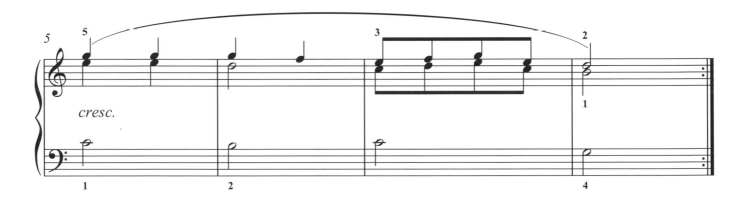

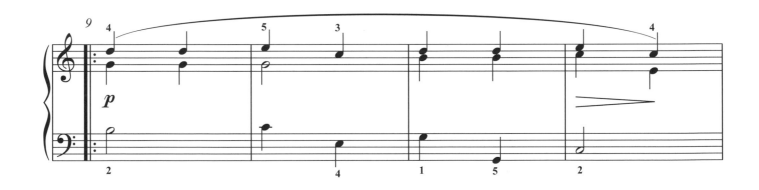

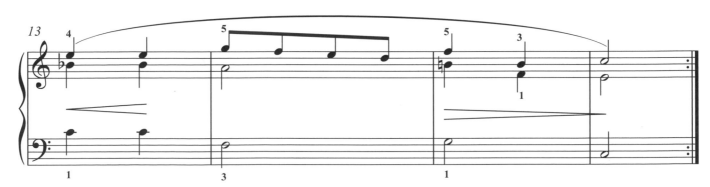

26. First Instructor

Op. 599, No. 15

Evenness Study: 2

Carl Czerny (1791-1857)

27. Practical Finger Exercises

Op. 802, No. 9

Sustaining Fingers / Independence of Each Individual Finger

Carl Czerny
(1791-1857)

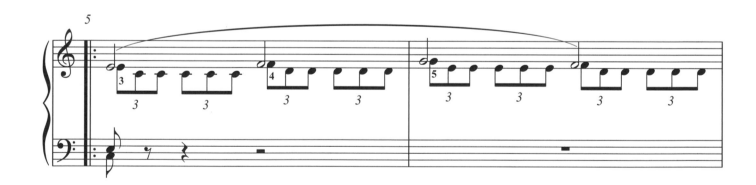

28. Practical Finger Exercises

Op. 802, No. 1 & 4

Finger Strength and Equalization of all Fingers: 3
Transpose these exercises also in E Minor Scale (see p. 52) and D Minor Scale (see p. 62).

Carl Czerny (1791-1857)

29. Rhythmic and Melodic Etude

Op. 105, No. 20

Theodor Kirchner (1823-1903)

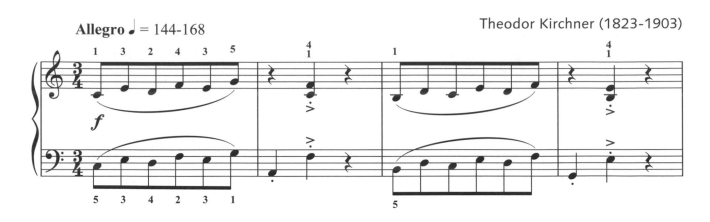

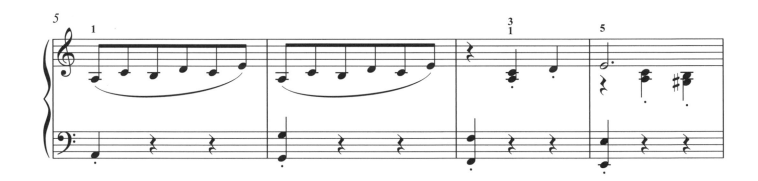

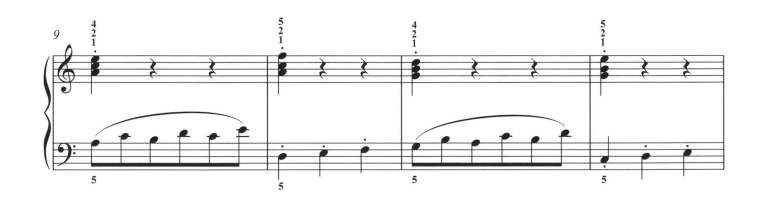

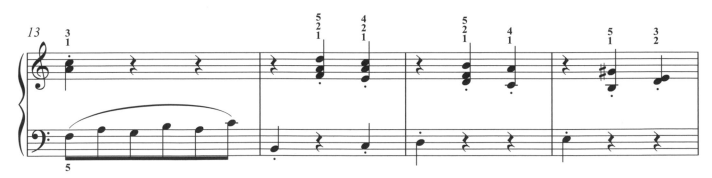

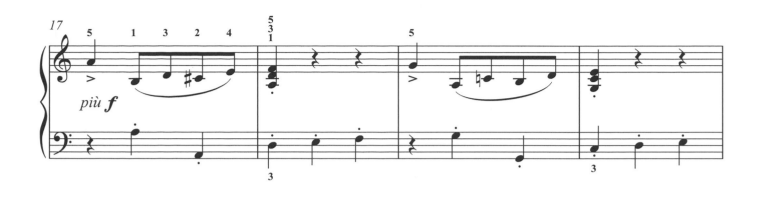

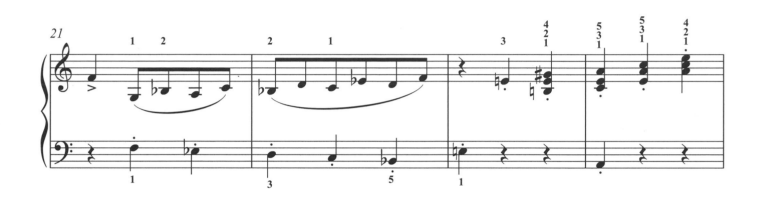

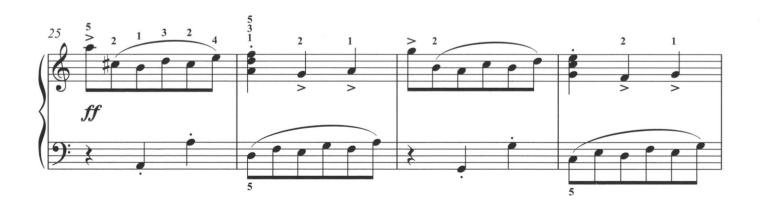

30. Étude Enfantine

Op. 37, No. 10

Jean-Henry Lemoine (1786-1854)

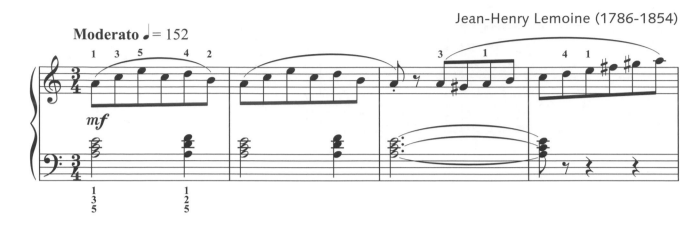

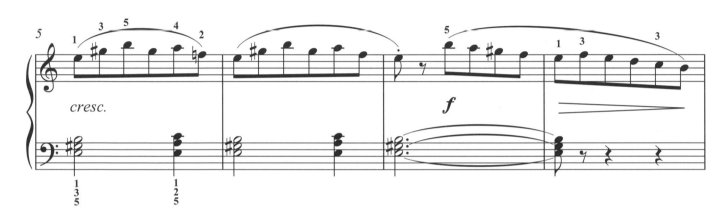

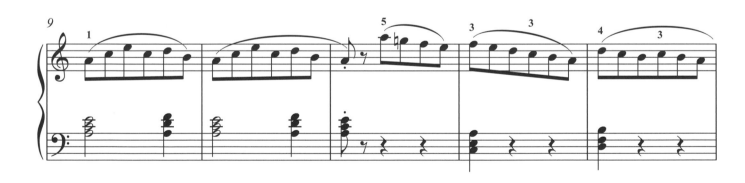

Fine

D. C. al Fine

31. Preparatory School

Op. 101, No. 91

Allegretto ♩ = 96

Ferdinand Beyer (1803-1863)

32. Elementary Study

Op. 176, No. 5

Velocity Study: 3

Allegro moderato ♩ = 144-168

Jean-Baptiste Duvernoy (1800-1880)

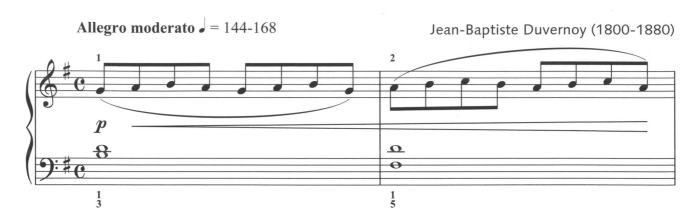

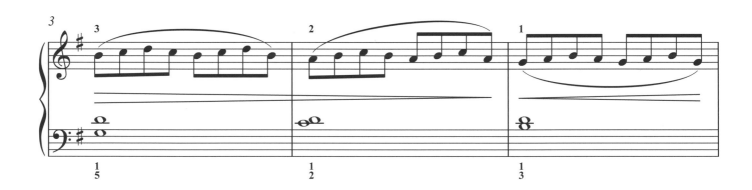

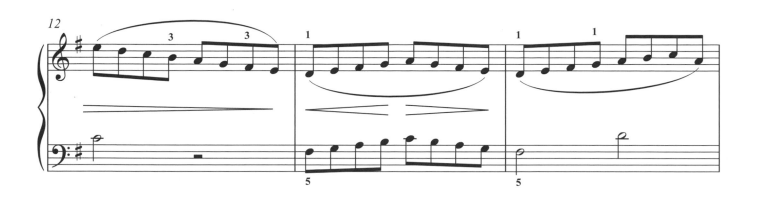

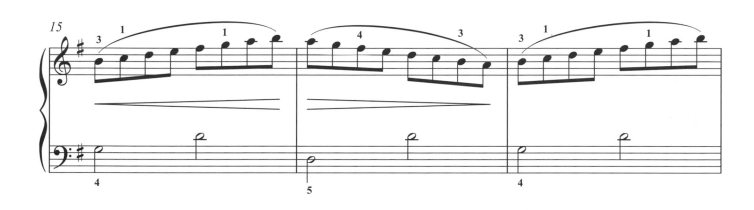

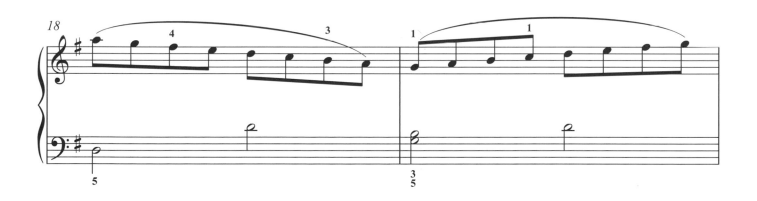

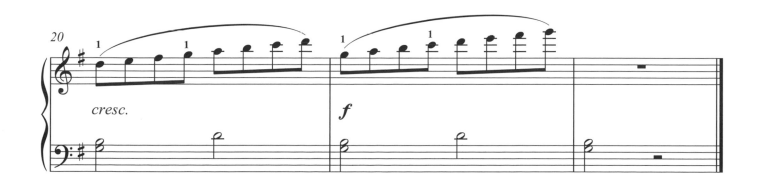

33. Syncopation Studies

Syncopation on Second Count

Hans-Günter Heumann

Syncopation on Third Count

Syncopation on Fourth Count

34. Preparatory School

Op. 101, No. 94

Allegretto ♩ = 80

Ferdinand Beyer (1803-1863)

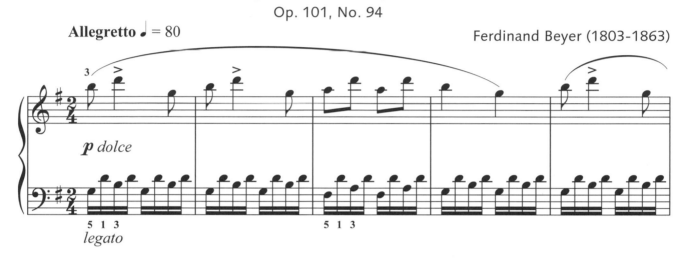

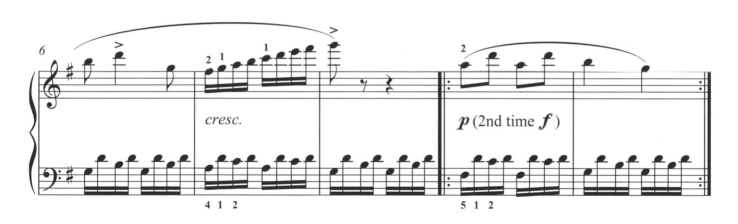

35. Easy Study

Op. 108, No. 8

Evenness and Articulation Study: 1

Moderato con moto ♩ = 126

Ludvig Schytte (1848-1909)

36. Easy Study

Op. 108, No. 14

Evenness and Articulation Study: 2

Ludvig Schytte (1848-1909)

37. Elementary Study

Op. 176, No. 12

Interchange between the Hands: 2

Moderato ♩. = 96

Jean-Baptiste Duvernoy (1800-1880)

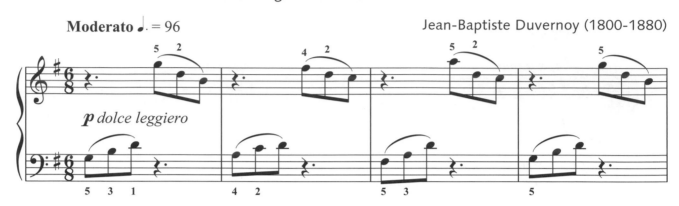

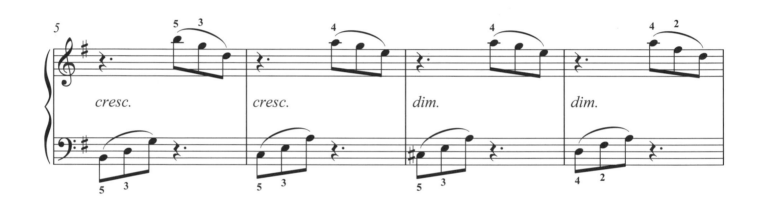

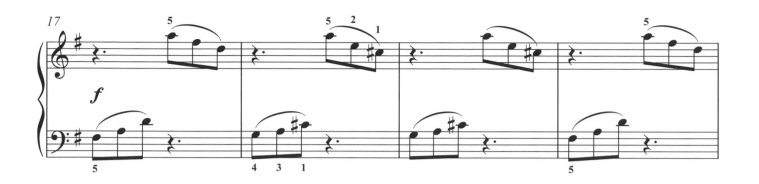

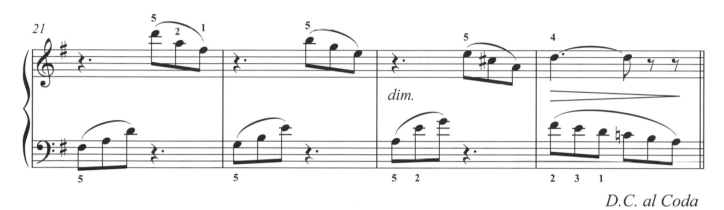

D.C. al Coda

Coda

*) Arpeggio (Ital. la arpa = harp) is a performance instruction for keyboard, plucked and bowed instruments, indicating that the notes of a chord should not be played at the same time, but one after another - 'broken' - in the way they would sound when played on a harp, usually ascending from the lowest to the highest note.

38. Finger Strength and Equalization of all Fingers: 4

The Virtuoso Pianist, Exercise 2

Charles-Louis Hanon (1819-1900)

39. Finger Strength and Equalization of all Fingers: 5

The Virtuoso Pianist, Exercise 3

♩ = 100-168

Charles-Louis Hanon (1819-1900)

40. Little Melodic Exercise for Beginners

Op. 187, No. 54

Interchange between the Hands: 3

Moderato ♩ = 132

Cornelius Gurlitt (1820-1901)

Fine

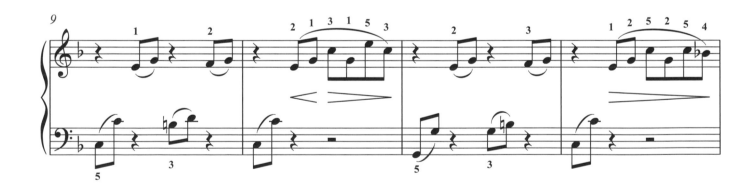

D. C. al Fine

41. Innocence

Study Op. 100, No. 5

Evenness and Articulation Study: 3

Friedrich Burgmüller
(1806-1874)

42. Preparatory School

Op. 101, No. 98

Evenness and Articulation Study: 4

Ferdinand Beyer
(1803-1863)

43. Easy Exercise

Op. 139, No. 30

Marcia. Allegro maestoso ♩ = 96

Carl Czerny (1791-1857)

44. Little Melodic Exercise for Beginners

Op. 187, No. 50

Chord Study: 4

Cornelius Gurlitt (1820-1901)

Vivace ♩. = 84

45. Solfeggio*)

Chord Study: 5

Carl Philipp Emanuel Bach
(1714-1788)

*) Solfeggio (Ital. or Fr. Solfège) is a method of sight singing using the syllables do (originally ut), re, mi, fa, sol (or so), la and si (or ti) to represent the pitches of the scale. Solfeggio singing exercises are usually virtuoso, similar to the keyboard works of some Baroque composers.